HARD
LINES

First published in 1983
by Faber and Faber Limited
3 Queen Square London WC1N 3AU
Printed in Great Britain
by Redwood Burn Ltd. Trowbridge Wiltshire

This selection © Faber and Faber Limited 1983

British Library Cataloguing in Publication Data
Hard Lines
    1. English literature
    I. Title
    820.8   PR1109
    ISBN 0-571-13073-9

Hard Lines would have been impossible without help from Fanny Dubes,
Anne Clarke, and The Small Back Room.

HARD LINES
NEW POETRY AND PROSE

About this book

Until lately it has been secret. The truth is now plain for all to see.

(Where there is a will there is a way)

We all have brains and feelings

We are all equally

  capable

  of changing the world

  by creating a world of our own.

Not everybody has noticed yet.

Many countries are less free than we.

We will either die a nuclear death or we will not.

Looking on the bright side, perpetual progress is inevitable.

Famine and disease are on the wane in spite of everything.

In spite of 5 million children dying of dysentery in India every year.

(Three-quarters of the world's disease will be eradicated when clean water systems are provided. This will cost a quarter of what the world spends on alcohol each year.)

Good luck to all of us.

Guns and bombs will die as the human spirit prospers.

The revolution begins in the living-room.

As technology phases out all human involvement with production,
many millions of unemployed persons will have to discover interests
within themselves

or die of boredom and madness.

Hobbies and leisure activities will acquire a new and true important
place in the structure of society. Being a creative artist will no longer be
the guarded and privileged occupation of the few; it will become the norm.

Absorbing and demanding self-employment will be the order of the day.

Music, drawing, writing and fun will be compulsory school subjects
from the age of 3. There will be rock 'n roll colleges, creative life colleges,
sex colleges, mountaineering colleges, model airplane colleges. Pure and
applied beauty will be a high field of study, ultimately even enabling us
to cherish mass-produced items.

Manual labour will become a healthy weekend pastime.

Britain, because it is comparatively gentle and reasonably well off, will
be the first nuclear power to opt out of the insanity of war, and into the
exciting wonderments of future peace.

This being so, the quicker everybody realizes it, the quicker we ban
the bleeding bomb, and
within fifty years the whole world will be united and engaged in
being happy.
This is certain to happen if we don't explode. Believe it or not,
believe it or not.
Leadership is nothing more than a twenty-four-hour wank. Self-control
is the modern way.
Self-fulfilment is our birthright and our shared gift of life. We do not all
need to be posers or artists or doctors, but we do all need to change the
world by learning how to enjoy it.
I really dig many of the pieces in this book.
Each writer makes me feel that life is worth living.
I'm a hopeless case I cannot read or write or paint
    a hopeless case My heart and nerves are faint
    a hopeless case I have a bad complaint
    a hopeless case Oh no I fucking ain't.

Ian Dury

TEENAGE POEMS CRUMPLED AT THE BACK OF MY DRAWER

Sensible now – settled down
someone talking about control
well I've been fucked around so much
I just don't want the responsibility
and I'd forgotten I ever wanted to change
the world until I read
teenage poems
crumpled at the back of my drawer

Relaxed at work – steady employment
so glad I've got it together
I never thought I would get this far
people moving around me good morning
I wonder if you have
teenage poems
crumpled at the back of your drawer

Coming home I'm caught in the rush
someone smiles at me ... probably a pervert
it's good to be normal
it's nice to be nice
I'm a little tired
and I think about the past
and I remember
teenage poems
crumpled at the back of my drawer

I must tear them up
little pieces of petty emotion – who cares?
I regret keeping them writing them reading them
I'm home I look
at the wife at the kids at the TV
at the papers at myself in the mirror
in my room so this is life my wife
walks in and points at an open drawer
and burst into tears and I hold her
"Oh God," she weeps,
"teenage poems
crumpled at the back of your drawer."

John Maley

I'M WATCHING ALL THE CARS GO BY

I'm watching all the cars go by
I'm jumping at every phone
I'm lying awake for half the night
But still you don't come home
I wish I knew just why you went
I wish I'd seen the signs
But I was much too blind to see
Too late to read between the lines
I deserve an explanation
I deserve much more than this
I deserve to have you here with me
But is it you I miss?
Perhaps it's just the body
That used to lie on my right-hand side
Perhaps it's just your voice
That tended to grate when I was tired
Perhaps I don't miss you at all
Perhaps that's what you've always known
Perhaps I'm not being honest enough
Is that why you won't phone?
I don't like messy endings
I like it all to be cut and dried
Is that what you hated most
To tell me? Perhaps you tried
There's lots of life left yet to live
There's a lot left in me to give
Why didn't I try it out on you?
I wonder who you're with ...

Jenny Fraser

LONDON TONIGHT

The avenues are beckoning
They say the time is right
The restaurants are waiting for
The people of the night

In search of entertainment
The painted faces pass
While shadows of nonentity
Will walk the broken glass

They say there is no poverty
The poor cannot be found
Yet I have heard the whispers
On every Underground

They say the drinks are flowing
The lights are shining bright
But I don't really feel
Like London tonight

Martin Tiernan

Andy Bylo

THEY SAY THEY'RE ONLY DOING THEIR DUTY

10

Them eyes watch you
Till you don't feel no pride
Them eyes watch you
Nowhere to hide
Them eyes gonna get you
Not much time
Them eyes will catch you
You're next in line
And when them eyes grab you
It's useless to attack
Them eyes don't care nothin'
To them we're "fucking black".

Carlene Montoute

I'LL TELL YOU WHO HE IS

I'll tell you who he is
he's the maggot in the half-eaten apple
he's the crack in the dam
he's the damp in the freshly cut timber
he's the stain on the wall
he's the lump on the woman's breast
he's the bullet in the assasin's gun
he's the wart on the pretty girl's mouth
he's the mud in the goalmouth
he's the hair on the model's legs
he's the dirt underneath your fingernail
he's the starvation in the child's belly
he's the greed on the fat boy's face
he's the lust in the rapist's eyes
he's the oil on the seagull's feathers
he's the nail on the Cross
that's who he is

Graham Adcock

SALLY

You meant nothing to me
that first time we met,
your hair was greasy
your back was wet.
You weren't really cheap
or really that dear,
but you were to cost me
the best part of a year.

I remember sometimes
I could wait for up to
half an hour
freezing cold or getting
wet in a midsummer shower.
I remember your innocent smile
if I mentioned sex or food,
your tender gentle blindness
could melt my vilest mood.

The warmth of my last token
now hangs limp, crinkle and twist
represented by a silver chain
that hangs upon her wrist.
I never knew what she felt for me
all men fear the truth,
was love between us
or was it simply youth?

John Hollingsworth

MANIFESTO

I disown word-games.
I despise academic constipation.
I'm sick of literary incest.
I want to write poems fuelled by anger.
I want poems grimed with perspiration,
poems that leak like mildew
through tenement walls,
poems punctuated by
the rhythm of factories,
poems of insolence,
poems that belch from
industrial chimneys showering
cities like syllables,
poems that thumb noses.
I want poems that slum children
can play with in gutters.
I want poems to chalk on the
walls of condemned buildings.
I want poems of hope for those
who slouch on street corners.
I want poems to be chanted at picket lines,
poems set to the metre that measures despair,
poems to inspire insurrection against inequality,
poems that explode myths like neons at midnight,
poems encapsulating hopelessness.
I want poetry that is real.

Andrew Darlington

PRODUCTION LINE

Swarms of people
Voices grate together
Machines spilling oil
Stale smell
Noise biting
Eating nerve ends
Jeyes Fluid
Sweat
Lights burning like
Hot pokers stroking eyes
Stuffy
Sick joke
Cackling laughter
Feeling ill
Sounds accelerating
Crescendo into screams
My screams
Silent screams
Stuck in my throat
Back aching
Shoulders on fire
Head spinning
Room growing dim
Trolleys spewing cloth
People
Blending into one
Revolving
Turning upside-down
Hands tired
Trying to move faster
Ever quicker
Dizzy

Brain twisting
Surroundings hazy
Speed = work = wages
Sick welling
Churning inside my stomach
Faint
Bell ringing
Relief
Outside
Clean air
Lungs bursting freshness
Sun smiling
Content
Until tomorrow
When repetition repeats
Again and again and again ...

Debbie Radford

Andy Bylo

PLEASE PLEASE ME

Promise never to leave me
Lie, cheat or otherwise deceive me
And don't run around with my best friend
It would drive me daft – clean round the bend

If I'm bad in bed please please fake it
Never tell the truth, I couldn't take it
Don't ignore me when I greet you
and please turn up when I'm waiting to meet you

Don't break my heart and steal my pride
Tear me apart and kill me inside
Because that's the day I'll turn and flee
The day you turn round and behave like me

James Kelly

OLD PHOTOGRAPHS

Eyes that have no destiny.
Faces that have no past.
Anonymous.
Thin-faced children who grew old and died.
Old men with long beards tottering off on crutches
    to paradise.
Firm-hipped women who bred generations.
Sailors with brine on their faces.
Soldiers with the Somme on their minds.
Identities time ripped like rain-rotted newspapers
Yellow with age.
Names, pastless, futureless, homeless.
Scattered embers with sparks captured.
Dead pale shadows with memory's soil forgotten.
Going nowhere. Coming from nowhere.
Lost in time and pitiful.

David Fields

LOVE

Breathe gently on love do not disrupt the
Feather-thin cover that protects
The young lovers.

Tracy Watt

MAYBE TOMORROW

Maybe tomorrow
Sooner or later I'll forget. Maybe
Tomorrow the pain will go and I'll
Be able to throw out all those
Old love letters. Maybe tomorrow
I'll be able to face your smile,
Your laughing eyes not laughing
At me not smiling at me
But at another.
Maybe tomorrow I'll take my life
Because the pain's too great and I'm weak without you.
Maybe tomorrow.

Tracy Watt

She was in the kitchen making the coffee, warming the rolls, when she heard the metallic click of the letter box. Hating to leave the warmth of the stove, she walked into the hallway and stared at the letter lying face-down on the mat. She stooped to pick it up and shivered. She put it in the pocket of her dressing-gown and returned to the kitchen, turned the oven to low and made two mugs of coffee, one with sugar. She put them on a tray and stood the letter upright between them and walked quietly into the bedroom where the radio bantered inoffensively and he lay half-asleep or pretending; she never could tell.

"David," she whispered, "your letter; it's arrived." She placed it on the quilt and put his mug on the bedside table, moving a tiny jar of flowers out of the way. She sat on the side of the bed, holding her mug with both hands and she waited while he reached over the top of the covers. He seemed to burrow down further; she wondered how he could see to read. Nearly a minute passed before she heard him sigh. His long body seemed to curl up, away from her. She sipped nervously at her coffee and rubbed her calf for warmth. She listened to the radio announcer and envied his slick sentences. She watched the coffee grow cold, the milk puckering on the top. "I'm going into the kitchen. To read. It's warmer."

When she entered the bedroom to get ready for work she saw him sleeping. As she fixed her hair she peeked at the top of his head in the mirror. She chewed her lip and clattered her jewellery before she chose some to wear. She bounced down heavily on the side of the bed and tugged on her knee length boots. "Kate," he said and startled her. "What time is it?" She cleared her throat. "Almost four-thirty." Her voice sounded odd to her; she hadn't used

Candyce Lange

it all day. "I have to go now; have to be a bit early." Already she was anticipating the noise and the talk and she felt guilty. "David," she began. "I don't know what to say . . ." He touched her thigh with his forefinger. "Hey," he said softly. "You don't want to be late now. We'll talk about it later."

It was late when she returned, her face burning from running into the wind. The hall-light burned orange. "David?" she called, shaking her head loose from the hood of her coat. She opened the door of their room and saw the unmade bed. The room was lit by candlelight. He was sitting over by the window and she could see the misty green, then red of the traffic light. He sat in front of the one-barred electric heater; it grinned at her eerily. She looked at the small, empty liquor bottle standing by his bare feet. "You might get a cold with no socks on," she said. "How was it tonight?" "Oh, it went all right really. Look at all the tips I made." She knelt down beside him and pulled out of her mitten a dark silk scarf tied into a small bundle. She spread the four corners of the scarf on to the rug and started to count the coins. "How come the stereo's not on?" "I don't know; I couldn't think of anything I wanted to hear." She looked at the candles burning, trying to assess how long he'd been sitting there like that. "We could go out for breakfast tomorrow. Get the papers first and have a proper breakfast. Like we used to." She watched the expression around his mouth change slightly. She fingered the cool stack of coins. "Kate," he said and turned his body to face hers. He placed his arms around her neck, loosely; his hands were left dangling. "I know we need to talk. I know you're waiting for me to do something." She started to shake her head, then stopped herself.

They blew out all the candles except for the one they placed on the bedside table and allowed to burn into the night. Kate listened to him fall asleep first, the cotton material on his back feeling rough against her forehead, her hands pushed together flat between her legs, her knees bent inside the envelope of her flannel nightdress. She tucked her head under the covers and smelled their stale smell before she fell, finally, asleep.

In her dream, she could see strange green licks of flame rising from the concrete ground and small puddles of clear blue water near her. She could not feel the boundaries of her body. She did not feel the heat; only the panic. She tried to run but the flames were everywhere. She found herself sitting in one of the pools of water. Her brother was there and two other people she did not know. He offered her a large yellow tablet; it was round and smooth like a gumball. She stared at it lying in his palm. He told her that the flames would get higher, the pools of water would evaporate soon, their choices were limited. She could not form her mouth into any question or response. She heard the noise of an airplane, and she could see it, monstrous and black, slicing through the green flames, flying terrifyingly near to the concrete ground.

She woke up. She opened her eyes and her mouth fell open. She was lying on her back. The room was very dark and she knew that she was alone in the bed. "David," she cried out, sitting up, clawing the sheet beside her. The bedroom door opened immediately and he stood there, carrying a mug. The light from the hallway outlined him and made her blink. "I had a terrible dream." She could not look at his face. She looked at his legs in his old jeans and his bare feet. "Do you want the light on?" he asked. "Do you want a sip of this? It's chocolate."

18

Boyd Montgomery

SEMI-AUTOMATIC LOVE

Your love is like a neutron bomb
A total killer that's a fact
Your kisses blew my brain away
but left my lips intact

Your smile is like a laser gun
As bright as light can be
I'm as cold as a dull dead sun
Until you shine on me

Your mind is like a hand grenade
Throwing shrapnel all around
Your laughter like a fusillade
Shot me to the ground

Your heart is like an armoured car
Protected from all danger
A sentry calling "Who goes there?"
Don't treat me like a stranger

James Kelly

THE ONLY THING BETWEEN US IS TIME

Something turned in my mind last night
and told me not to cry
I don't know if I'm right
even though I try
After all my years of wandering
alone within my world
it's hard to think you want to share
the dream that I unfold
And I hope this will be forever
and we'll always be together
Maybe tomorrow you might change your mind
The only thing between us is time

Gently lying close to you
sleeping on the floor
hoping one day we'll come through
and open every door
Lights are flashing on and off
and I need someone to hold
It's hard to think that you're not just
a story I've been told
And I hope this will be forever
and we'll always be together
Maybe tomorrow you will see a sign
The only thing between us is time

In the morning when the sun returns
I'll wake you with a kiss
while my hearts sits outside and yearns
Where can we go from this
We've been so far I've held you near
all through the rain and snow
I can't believe that you're still here
even though you're free to go
And I hope this will be forever
and we'll always be together
Maybe tomorrow you will break the line
The only thing between us is time

Dave Greaves

19

BEDSIT SUICIDE

20

Walls decorated with torn posters
Trying to brighten up the damp room
That single room that is called home
On the third floor of a decaying Victorian emblem.
The landlord comes once a week
An anonymous shark in an expensive suit
Exploiting the needs of an increasing market
"Problem with the meter, I'll get it seen to."
Next week, next month, next year, who knows?
Does he care? But then again, do you?
Cold and depressing, lonely and bleak
Come home from work and stare at the walls
Thinking of your home town, it wasn't so bad
But here in the metropolis, no one to call friend,
Just acquaintances, an occasional drink
Then back to that room which you start to dread
Start thinking about tomorrow, you hope it won't come
You decide that it won't, not for you anyway
Three days before you are found
Autopsy report, drugs overdose.

Paul K. Hockley

NOCTURNAL NIGHTMARE

Three in the morning
Burning eyes
Can't stop yawning
Endless sighs.

Getting too old
To be up all night
Won't be told
What's wrong or what's right.

Vodka's nearly all gone
Stories running dry
Get the coffee on
Loosen my tie.

Dawn breaks through the haze
Another day,
Brain muddled, in a daze
What a price to pay.

Paul K. Hockley

A HOUSE DEFILED

At morning
   Four!
They came, and not to see
   the milk-shone sun
Rise over grey and dusted town.
Committee-sent,
   two stoned-faced youths
Stood guard the rear with
   truncheons held and ordered
Fear
   across their thin and hair-groomed lips.
Beneath sharp peaks hid
   shadowed eyes of darkened want.
"Open up!"
   their sergeant yelled
And flicked his wrist.
My door was felled, a plywood
   tree hung sadly
   kicked on single hinge
And up the narrow stair they came.
"Up! Up! Up!"
   the mastiff yelled ...
And my wife fell back
   to open the door.
Her small white fists press tight to teeth,
   unspoken fear.
Reflected in the polished boards,
   inverted, blue and anger-shaped
Shone hatred
   from the wooden floor.
And I,
   held tight, back to a wall

By stubborn wick bit
   fingered press.
Intoned correct but cold, a call ...
   "What ... do you know?"
And into my room the Captain stepped.
He touched my book
   in browsing flicks.
"This," he said,
   "is not allowed and men
Have died for less."
   He smiled.
"Be warned."
And out they filed.

Joy Rogers

HACKETT VANESSA CARRUTHERS

Vanessa Carruthers was hackett. Pot-ugly. A dog. And she knew it. "Don't worry, Vanessa," said her mother, kindly. "It's not a person's looks that counts but what they are like inside – their personality."

"Thank fuck for that," replied Vanessa, "I really am hackett!"

Nothing Mrs Carruthers said gave Vanessa any real hope, though, because it didn't change the fact that she was ugly. Dogsville, Tennessee. No amount of make-up could make her attractive. At school none of the teachers liked her because she was ugly. Boys never asked her out. They never whistled after her as she walked along the corridors of the school. No one ever offered to carry her books home from school. Right enough, someone had said she looked like Jane Fonda. From the back. With a duffle coat on. With the hood up. During an eclipse. Merci beaucoup, thought Vanessa. Merci fucking beacoup.

Vanessa's ugliness depressed her. She seemed to spend half her time contemplating the void and the other half contemplating suicide. She remembered the time she had written to Hang-Ups magazine about her problem. They had suggested she ask a boy out. Vanessa plucked up enough courage, with the aid of a half-bottle of vodka, to ask out a boy she fancied at school. "Would you like to go to a party with me?" she had asked him.

"Fuck off you dog!" he had replied. "I wouldn't put the boot in you, you ugly cow!"

Vanessa was getting fed up with this victimization. So she was ugly. Big wow! She wasn't the only hackett person in the world! "Vanessa, looks don't matter," a classmate had told her. Her classmate just happened to be absolutely beautiful. Vanessa hated that 'looks don't matter but thank fuck I'm gorgeous' attitude.

It wasn't fair. No one liked Vanessa because she was a dog. But she was the absolute salt of the earth. "It's not fair!" she complained to her school counterparts. "I'm the salt of the earth!"

"You can't fuck kindness," they had replied. But surely sex wasn't everything?

"Sex isn't everything," retorted Vanessa, "Anyway you don't look at the mantlepiece when you're poking the fire! It's so unjust. All I want is a bit of respect. Okay, so I'm not the most sexually attractive person in the world." Everyone nodded. "But beauty isn't everything. It's time facial discrimination was stamped out. I'm fed up with being made the butt of people's crude jokes because of my ugliness. What kind of society is it that places looks above a person's character? A sick society, that's what kind! I'm fucking hackett: big deal! So none of you guys have an overwhelming urge to fuck me. Well, you can go and have a wank, then. Just don't go insulting me, you creeps! Just because I'm an ugly dog. Inside I'm really a beautiful person. I'm hackett, any objections?"

"I think you're nice, Vanessa," confessed a classmate.

"Thanks," replied Vanessa. She walked along the corridor, hackett but proud.

John Maley

CANAL

When we were kids
We used to play
Along the canals.
And in summer
We'd catch sticklebacks
And guess how deep it really was;
Laugh and joke with the barge hands,
Take rides up to the docks;
Under bridges, past factories
To the wide River Thames.
But they closed the canal –
The saws stopped cutting
And the timber rotted
In the silent deserted mills –
Drained it somehow
And filled it with dirt.
With every shovel-load
They buried my childhood
To create a landscaped park
For muggers and lovers,
But they'll never take away
My memories.

I. L. Josland

HEATWAVE

Why not frizzle yourself
to a medium rare
cover virgin flesh in Ambre Solaire?
Hairy chest or singed nipple,
two melted choc ices or a raspberry ripple.

Me aunt got burnt,
caused quite a commotion –
smother on tenderly the calamine lotion.
It's much to do about nothing
for two bloody days,
getting voluntarily abused
by infra-red rays.

Look at them in the park,
packed tit to arse.
The sun turns society
into a deodoranted farce.
Sawn-offs, flip-flops, sandals and shades,
the grass dry and sharp
like a flick-knife blade.

With little white tops
they flaunt third-degree burns,
pathetic swollen flesh –
won't they ever learn?
It's the same every year:
"Just a quick sunbathe."
Pseudo-masochists' delight,
it's a British heatwave.

John Hollingsworth

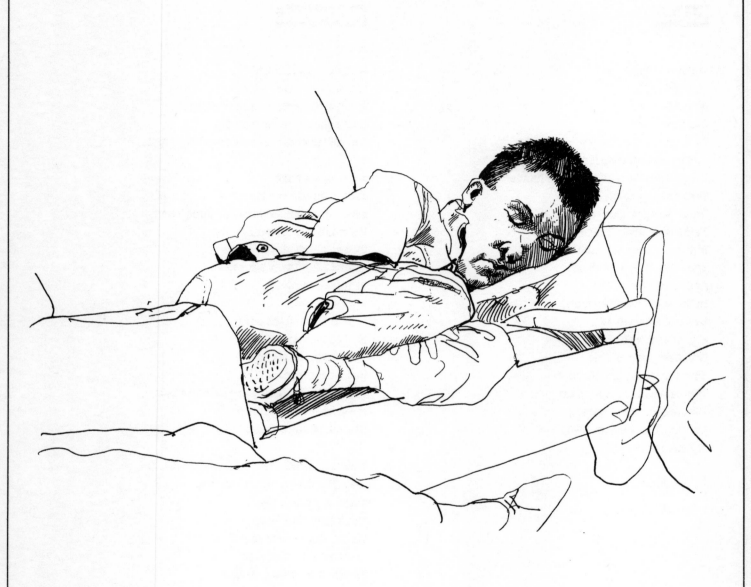

Andy Bylo

WAITING-ROOM

Lying on top of her bed
but not relaxing
Judy stares at the paint
flaking on the ceiling
and wipes away a tear
she wants happiness

For Judy, in her life,
there is no waiting-room

Hands all shaky
holding a toy gun
Harry stares at the shopkeeper
he's drunk on whisky
is on the dole
and he wants money

For Harry, in his life,
there is no waiting-room

Crushing his fag
under his foot
Alex coughs up catarrh
and walks out of the jobcentre
he doesn't want socialism
he just wants revenge

For Alex, in his life,
there is no waiting-room

Three of the belt
bastards!
Susan had only forgotten a jotter
she doesn't know what $2x + 3y + 6z$ equals
and they'll make her suffer for it
she wants education – not subjugation

For Susan, in her life,
there is no waiting-room

Kicks from glue and beer
signing on
depressed and disillusioned
wandering the streets

John Maley

SAND CASTLES

Bloody beaches
Burning boats
Blood-soaked leeches
Parched dry throats
Proscribed books
Secret signs
Dirty looks
Filthy minds
Suntan lotions
Tidal waves
Late-night notions
Tribal braves
Custard 'n kippers
Boarding-house blues
Drunken day-trippers
Sand in their shoes
Priests, nuns, the Holy Ghost
Taking the water
For a day at the coast.

James Kelly

WHO'S EXPLOITING WHO?

My skin is black
Her skin is white.
Her hair is silky
My hair is tight.

You say you use her
But it's her that's using you.
Take what she offers –
Who's exploiting who?

And when you lie beside her
With no one else to see,
Don't start feeling guilty
Over poor rejected me.

Her hair is silky
My hair is tight.
My skin is black
Her skin is white.

You say she's a loser
But deep down we know it's you,
So take all her money, love –
Who's exploiting who?

Carlene Montoute

FOR FUTURE PRESENTATION...
(TEATIME IN HOLLYWOOD)

Through the swirling sea-spray,
sprawls Uncle Joe's refreshing seaside café,
standing still like an abrupt regiment against the sky.
Inside (it's so nice to see)
everyone's starstruck with Uncle Joe's 4p-a-cup tea:
stone me – even Richard Burton!
Directors dance around in an orderly disorder,
with plenty to say,
plenty to feel ('cos the night is still warm and friendly);
everyone except Stamp.
He's squatting in a spidery corner,
god, what a mess,
looking like maximum death.

The adventurous ocean-going trippers delight
themselves in swearing,
at a cut-out vision of Stamp, who's staring,
at millions of pairs of Levis,
millions of crabby legs,
millions of life-like sweet-boy faces (all of them small).
Nothing escapes from his pointless penetrations.

The boulevard crosses the path next to the
ancient lighthouse-keeper,
who's staring transfixed at the Titanic stranded
on the beach,
washed up with the white whale and
the 2 a.m. tidal wave.

Flotsam and jetsam hover around the
cool mint-chocolate shores,
as the neatly defined lighthouse reflection
flicks across 007's brand new electronic
double-decker,
just next to where our gracious Titanic
broke a million hearts on an ice-breaker.
And the stars are born,
and the stars are innocent;
the stars don't capsize;
and the stars don't drink.
The stars don't function,
but never break up ... and never sink.
But she'd fooled everyone completely;
everyone except Stamp, and maybe a few others.
'Cos I saw them walking away leaving
footprints as big as their grins,
pissing themselves, and waving goodbye to all
who had the pleasure of accompanying
her onboard,
and teatime waved goodbye to Hollywood.

Aidan Cant

IDEAL PARTNERS

He comes in from work at half-five, sits in his favourite
chair by the fire and reads the paper

She comes in from work at half-six, struggling with the
week's shopping and coping with a headache

He says, "Hello, darling, put the kettle on while you're out
there, will you? I'm dying for a cuppa"

She throws the shopping to the floor with an almighty crash
as she fights for some kind of control

He thinks to himself, "Butter fingers," and turns to the
sports page

She regains control and brings his tea five minutes later

He calls "Oh darling, you forgot to sugar it"

She forgets all about control as she watches the sugar bowl
whizz through the living-room and miss his nose by
an inch

He thinks, "Hello, pre-menstrual tension"

She goes into a dreamlike trance and starts putting the
shopping away

He's in the middle of reading Bill Shankley's obituary when
he says "Oh darling, I almost forgot, I invited Jeremy
and Linda over for dinner tonight, you don't mind,
do you?"

She feels something snap quite suddenly inside her and
hardly realizes that she's throwing china, tins of beans
and tomatoes at the kitchen walls

He thinks, "Yes, definitely pre-menstrual tension," and
decides to see if he can rescue some sugar

She kneels on the floor and tries slashing her wrists with
the kitchen scissors

He says, fatherly, "Oh darling, you know those scissors are
blunt, remember the difficulty you had last night trying
to cut the sausages, I told you to get them sharpened

She swings round and makes a wild attempt at stabbing
him in the stomach; she misses as he moves towards
the sugar

He says, "It's no use giving them to me, darling, I'm much
too busy at work to bother about such things as
sharpening scissors," and, having found the sugar,
returns to the living-room

She rushes to the bedroom and bashes her head against the
picture window, then vigorously shakes her head from
side to side so that the shard of glass beneath her neck
slits the jugular vein

He hears the smash of glass and says, "I hope you haven't
broken the picture window, darling," and then, going to
the bedroom, adds, "You know what an expense and a
bother it is to get it replaced, not to mention the work of
putting it in"

She hangs out of the window, now completely lifeless, with a
pool of blood beneath her feet

He thinks, "There you see, I was right all along,
pre-menstrual tension," then, with a smug smile, sits
back in his favourite chair, puts two sugars in his tea
and turns to the TV page

Claire Dowie

THE THICKNESS OF ICE

At first we will meet as friends
(Though secretly I'll be hoping
We'll become much more
And hoping that you're hoping that too).

At first we'll be like skaters
Testing the thickness of ice
(With each meeting
We'll skate nearer the centre of the lake).

Later we will become less anxious to impress,
Less eager than the skater going for gold,
(The triple jumps and spins
Will become an old routine:
We will be content with simple movements).

Later we will not notice the steady thaw,
The creeping cracks will be ignored,
(And one day when the ice gives way
We will scramble to save ourselves
And not each other).

Last of all we'll meet as acquaintances
(Though secretly we will be enemies,
Hurt by missing out on a medal,
Jealous of new partners).

Last of all we'll be like children
Having learnt the thinness of ice,
(Though secretly, perhaps, we may be hoping
To break the ice between us
And maybe meet again as friends).

Liz Loxley

I WILL BE YOUR ARMALITE

When a bullet is fired from an Armalite AR15 rifle it travels 3,285 feet a second; at a third of a mile it will pierce both sides of a steel helmet and leave a hole the size of a fist in a man's head (Observer, August 1975)

I will be your Armalite,
flesh-tearing, life-devouring.
Stalking midnight Belfast alleys
where burning bus barricades
fill concrete canyons of urban
flyovers with arabesques of flame.
Crimson gnawing at sky,
at streets, at rooftops,
reflected in lenses,
in shattered glass, in pools of blood,
in faces gauging patterns of light and shade.
I will be your Armalite,
firm at your shoulder, recoil-absorbing,
growing hot and trembling
beneath the caress of your fingers,
opening to you, accepting each
magazine clip pregnant with death.

Cradle me with your need,
feed me with your thirst,
and I will destroy for you,
death-pouring, fear-spawning,
white-flame spitting,
splitting shadows, splitting silence,
splitting bone.
Armalite tearing, Armalite maiming,
Armalite devouring clean baptisms of flame,
purging cities in the white heat of vengeance,
chanting litanies in terse bursts
of cyclic angry precision.
I will be your Armalite.
I will be your Armalite.

Andrew Darlington

OBJET D'ARTEFACT

You said you loved me,
You lied, lied, lied.
You said you loved me.
What you meant was I made you feel good.
You've got dresses in your wardrobe that make you
    feel good.

What do you do with dresses when they don't make you feel
    good any more?
You make dusters of them and polish your mirror so you
    can see your face.
I didn't deserve that courtesy.
You turned your back on me.
    I no longer existed.

You said you needed me.
You lied, lied, lied.
You said you needed me.
What you meant was that you needed a key,
A key to open the door to let you escape from home.
A key to open the door to your body.
A key to open the door to self-assurance and a sense
    of identity.

What do you do with keys you don't need any more?
You leave them lying at the bottom of your handbag.
And every once in a while you accidentally pick them up,
    hold them, your warm breath
    condensing on the cold, hard, dead surface
    and you remember these doors
    and smile.

I didn't deserve that courtesy.
I was left,
Left in the last door which had to be opened.
Forgotten,
I no longer exist.

James Kelly

TERMINAL TEDIUM

The sickness comes in three stages.

In the first stage the patient defies the disease.
He'll meet your eye and with steady voice
Say, I'm a qualified man, I'll have the job of my choice.
And jobs that he wants, there's damn few of these.

Confidently approaching interviews,
He's only one of eight or ten
In best Burton suits and shiny shoes.
But there's only one job. Disappointed again.

Days become weeks, March becomes May.
Hopes are fading, dreams slowly dying.
Feeling so old, got to keep trying,
And grey sleepless night greets grey empty day.
In the second stage the patient fights the disease
Afraid of the scrap heap, driven by fear,
He'll take any job, forsake his career.
Bookie, brickie or even baker, but again there's damn few of these

Interview follows interview follows interview,
The Burton suit a badge of defeat.
His shoes are old and hurting his feet,
Hopelessly searching for something to do.

Stage three is the most painful to write:
No self-esteem or sense of pride,
His eyes are cold, he's dead inside,
Punch-drunk and beaten and out of the fight.

Boyd Montgomery

James Kelly

Andy took his mouth and nose away from the crisp-poke full of glue. Fuck that! Sitting on the canal bank, he stared at the filthy, polluted water. He stared at the thick green scum that covered the canal, it's surface occasionally broken by a rusty pram or car. He coughed, and spat phlegm into the water. What would Mr Watt say when he noticed Andy wasn't in Maths, Room 6, 1.10 – 2.30 p.m.? Fuck knows. Wanker! Andy shoved his mouth and nose back into his poke and inhaled deeply. A bumble-bee passed, a 'Kingy'. Pure Tops! Andy gasped, coughed, and threw the crisp-poke into the canal. It floated. He threw a stone at it. It missed.

Plop! Fuck that! He threw another one. Bullseye! Yes! Another one. Plop! Brilliant. Plop! Plop! Fuckin' plop! That bastard Watty will tell Mr Fisher and he'll tell my da. And he'll kick my arse. Wankers!

Puke. I'm going to puke. Andy staggered away from the canal towards the nearby quarry. Puddles everywhere. It was pissing last night. Hundreds of stones. I'm fucking stoned! Wow! Far out! He walked into a puddle. In the middle, it was a foot deep. He began splashing around. He jumped up in the air. Again and again. Pure Tops! It's shit in Mr Watt's class. He gives you the belt for fuck-all. Mrs Johnston's a fat cow. A pure, utter bore. ZZZzzZzzzZZZZzzzzZzzz. And that cunt Macdonald ... sadistic old bastard. I must have discipline in my class. Splash! I must have discipline in splash! my class I must have splash splash splash fuck that!

That baldy bastard Thornton. Thinks he's great. Weedsville, Arizona. Do you WANT the belt, boy? Do you LIKE getting the belt?

And all those fuckin' brainy cunts! Swots!

And Big Derek and all his pals. Walking round the playground taking every cunt's fags and dinner money. Pricks! School's crap!!!

Andy walked out of the puddle and over the bleak, cold, stone covered quarry. The sky was growing darker. I've to watch Mandy tonight while the Bastards go to the pub. Alcoholics. Andy staggered over towards the path which wound its way round the quarry. He fell, got up. I wish I had loads and loads of money. I wish I was RICH! He staggered on till he reached the path. It was a bit muddy. Muddy muddy... muddy. Andy slipped and fell on his arse. Aayaaa! He felt ill and turned to one side. He began to vomit. I'm going to die I'm going to fuckin' choke.

An old man hurried past. He stopped a few yards on, turned to look at Andy vomiting noisily, then hurried on. Probably has a knife. Thug. Fuck that! It began to rain. Andy began to cry.

Dear Mr Riddell, wrote Mr Fisher, I am deeply concerned about your son Andrew's poor attendance ...

John Maley

JONATHAN

Jon's got it wrong, but he's never been told
he's too old, he's just not worth the bother.

He says he thinks the world is tickety-boo.

Jon's in a house, called a home. He never moans,
he never groans, but he'll be there for years if
you ever need him.

He says he thinks that war is good for his nerves.

Jon's in a room, next to June, but he can't ever hear her,
be near her. He says he thinks June's his sister,
but she's just a close friend.

He says he thinks June would make a very good
    Prime Minister.

Jon takes his capsule, sits on a footstool,
thinks he should act the fool, but he's still hiding and
abiding by their rules.

He says he thinks the doctor is a nice man.

Jon's very sad, but when they say that he's mad,
it makes him glad, just to think they cannot
touch his mind – someone's been there already.

Jon's going home, so they say, to run and play his
own way, and meet his friends. They're round the bend,
but please don't tell him I said that.

He says he thinks they'll probably never notice
    him anyway.

Jon's in his home, on the phone, to his friends, all the day.
He says he thinks they never hear him anyway.

Aidan Cant

Andy Bylo

MR AVERAGE

Mr Average is five foot eight,
works for Plessey's
and he's never been late.
Mr Average drives a new Ford Escort;
he's known to his bank manager as twenty-two
    point nought.

Mr Average has a wife and a dog,
a corporation terrace
and an outside bog
and an average number of kids
(that's two point five).
His wife's pretty average —
she's just learned to drive.

Mr Average goes out
about three times a week,
hasn't got a temper
(in fact he's rather meek),
sees things he wants
but is content to gloat,
liberal with his money
and liberal with his vote.

Mr Average
doesn't read books,
just watches the telly,
doesn't do much exercise,
so he's got a large belly,
doesn't read papers,
just stares at the sun,
prepared to fantasize
over some tart's bum.

Mr Average is an average Englishman:
does as little work
for as much as he can.
When you pass a mirror
take a closer look too:
make sure Mr Average
isn't looking at you.

John Hollingsworth

A PLAY FOR TODAY

38

A Play for Today
Is performed down our street
By a man clenching fists to the sky,
A little old lady shuffling her feet
And the children that constantly cry.

A Play For Today
Is performed down our street
But the actors aren't Equity members;
They're the burnt-out remains in the shell of a life
That no one in this world remembers.

Anne Clark

MORE TALK

Mr Jones
    took some steps west
and saw,
    I'm almost sure,
The very best that
    his life held,
Wrapped tight
    in fright, a silk-spun web
And milked
    to death
    by talk.
"More talk," he sighed,
    "with which I contend,"
And sighed again.
    In sight, the end; with
Beaten brow he marked
    his pace.

Joy Rogers

Andy Bylo

POEM FOR THE ETERNAL OPTIMIST

If the day comes
when Newcastle to London takes $3\frac{1}{4}$ minutes
when Dracula loses his teeth and has to pay a visit to
    the dentist
when I find a shop that sells polka-dot shirts like the ones
    Bob Dylan used to wear
when the Guinness Book of Records becomes obsolete
when Anthony Newley reaches Strawberry Fair
when the world spins the other way and everybody flies off

If the day comes
when Syd Barrett announces that he's alive (and well)
when Newcastle Brown Ale comes in capsules
when the whole of the Tyne will be fit to swim in
when Russia liberates a nation
when Ronald Reagan is called Red Buttons
when the rats lead the Pied Piper of Hamlin
when Davy Crockett relinquishes his "King of the Wild
    Frontier" title
when all motherless kids will find real mums
when Michael Foot dyes his hair
when all the homeless will have a real home

If the day comes
when the word "war" is obliterated from the Oxford
    Dictionary
when the Mona Lisa paints a portrait of Leonardo da Vinci
when everyone has more to eat than need be
when the sun rains water and the rain waters sun
when young Jonathan takes his capsule sits on a footstool
    and the doctors say he's not a fool

If the day comes
when no one writes poems about "the system"
when everyone indulges in neighbourly love – even if it's
    only for a minute
when the only guns around are water pistols
when the only rockets are those manufactured by
    Standard Fireworks
when I renounce my copy of the Beatles' Revolver
    as rubbish
when tulips open on the stroke of midnight
when all men are no more equal than others
when scarecrows are not consigned to fields of barley
(when they are able to walk and not scare anything)
when no news is bad news:
and the day you won't say I'm someone special

If the day comes
if that day comes
I wonder where the hell I'll be?

Aidan Cant

THE WRECK

He sat huddled up on the cold stone floor,
Oblivious of the noisy tubes
Speeding past every few minutes –
Or so it seemed to the passers-by,
But all the time
They were there –
A haunting reminder of where he was.
The nagging feeling constantly
Ate its way through his head.
It wasn't right, he knew that,
But where else could he go?

His arm throbbed painfully –
It was the only reminder of what had happened
The night before.
He rolled up the sleeve of his dirty coat
And took a long hard look.
The small punctures were now very obvious
And his mother's face flashed before him.
He wanted to get out.
So wearily he rose and on shaky legs
Walked towards the exit.

"Psst!" someone called out.
He turned and walked towards them,
Knowing what it meant –
Another blurry vision of another painful night.
He wanted to leave
But his mother's face faded
And was replaced by the syringe.
Piccadilly now had him completely
In its grasp. There was no way out –
Not now.

Rachel Campbell

— Where are my bloody socks?

She raised her head and flung back a lock of hair that had been hanging in her eyes. There was no feminine vanity or subtlety in that movement; it was precise and functional. Her face was vacant with an almost feline detachment. Staring at her child, vague thoughts flitted across her mind: blue baby eyes, green bottles in a blue sea, the powdery whiteness of a butterfly crushed in the hand. The baby laughed hugely, his face disappearing in a wreath of wrinkles, his eyes, deep, blue and empty.

The thud of angry footsteps on the stairs, the living-room door banged open.

A young man stood in the doorway. His clear grey eyes were clouded in the first murmurings of anger, and his usual careless smile was replaced by a hardening of the mouth, an ugly fixed hardness of the lips. The customary swagger of his pose was absent; he stood in an ugly stubborn fashion. In his hand he held a pair of damp socks.

— They're bloody well wet, he exclaimed.

— That's not my fault. I've got to wash them, haven't I? Oh, wear the brown pair. Does it matter? Her tone was light, almost flippant. The formality of words was taut with meaning.

— How can I wear those? They've a great big hole in them. Nothing's ever bloody right in this house!

Her head turned quickly, a vixen, with lips turned up in a sneer, revealing hard white little teeth.

— How would you know? You're never here. The words came forth abruptly, snapping the air.

— All right, calm down. Who's got a cob on then 'cos I'm going out and you've gorra stay in? His voice patronized her, and yet he was scared.

David Newsome

He bent down and began to pull on his damp socks, which steamed slightly from the heat of the electric fire.

– No I haven't. Don't kid yourself. If I didn't want you to go out, you wouldn't! Her voice rose, became querulous, a bitter sound.

– Yeah, he said, glancing at her sideways, covertly. Again his tone was at once mocking, challenging and still fearful.

They had fought so often in their two years together. He had never thought it would be like this. The very way she held herself made him want to strike her. He did not want to upset her. And yet he wished to destroy her utterly. If only he could arouse her, make her turn to him even if only in anger. Shouting and blows; afterwards it would be all right. It always was. He waited.

Nothing happened. She sat in a stone-like fixity, unmoving, apart from him. She refused to respond to him, to acknowledge him. Her soft brown eyes grew harder, duller. The life in her seemed to depart, and she sat rocking her baby mechanically, unaware.

Why did he do it? Why was he like this? Weren't her troubles enough? Did she really have to fight him as well? He was going out, he would enjoy himself. What need had he to hurt her further?

Her lack of response unnerved him and he was disarmed in spirit. Hurriedly he pulled on his shoes and proceeded to tie his laces.

– They need polishing. Her voice was flat, dull.

–What? Oh yeah, I know. Doesn't matter.

He felt sheepish, ashamed. He got up and went out into the hall to fetch his jacket. A sudden surge of fondness for his wife overwhelmed him. He turned back to the doorway.

– Look I'll stay in if you want!

– It doesn't matter.

– All right, I'll see you.

Quickly he went out, shutting the door sharply behind him. Outside the evening air enveloped him in its warmth. She'll be fine, he thought, I'll get someone in to mind the kid and take her out the weekend. That'll cheer her up.

He felt better and his spirits rose at the thought of a night down the pub. A bevy, cards, chat with the lads. See Phil about a new engine for me car. He set off briskly, almost jauntily down the road, the cracked pavement disappearing under a swift click of feet.

And yet beneath the sound of that swaggering walk he was confused, dissatisfied, filled with a deep, vague, airy desire and regret that eluded his words. Why had he spoken to her so? Why say this thing or that? They were things that had given pain and he had never meant them. Why, then, had they been said? He felt that somewhere there was something he should know and yet did not.

LOVER OR FRIEND?

Whether I came
As lover or friend
I lacked the certainty
Of a relationship

I know we kissed
And we held hands
But lovers and friends
Make both demands

We shared some wine
We shared some bread
And later on
We shared your bed

But we shared no knowledge
Of who we were
In the social terms of
"Are he and her?"

We shared the darkness
The sounds from the street
And some time in the night
A hand crossed the sheet

"Halt who goes there,
Lover or friend?"
In the darkness I recognize you
As one and the same

Liz Loxley

INTER-CITY 125

Inter-City 125 flying through the countryside,
Everything just a blur,
Only stopping in drab, depressing stations,
Getting you there fast,
City to City on a 125.

Cutting your journey time,
No chance to appreciate what's left of the British country,
Still, we're all in a hurry,
Time is the only really important factor
City to City on a 125.

Amazing Technology,
Automatic Doors,
Speed Psychology,
Engine Roars,
That's City to City on a 125.

Paul K. Hockley

NIGHTMARE

Standing in the shower
After last night's nightmare
Horrified because the cold sweat
Won't wash away
(Even after using Lifebuoy)
Scared because I thought
That I hadn't woken up
Looking out of the steamed bathroom window
Rank upon rank of uniformed slums
Cramped backyards and overflowing dustbins
Permanent cloud of smoke
Consecutively ejected from the ironworks
Maybe I never went to sleep in the first place?

Debbie Radford

UNREQUITED LOVE

Why are you mine in dreams only
And his to hold in fond embrace
Why are my nights so cold so lonely
Every second every minute seeing your face

I long to cradle you in my arms and
Taste the sweetness of your breath
I long to woo you, win you with my charms
Never to lose you not even in death

I have a love we'll never share
A song we'll never sing
For if I reach out I know you're not there
Unrequited love is a woeful
Wonderful thing

James Kelly

MONDAY'S CHILD

46

Monday's child has lost his face
Tuesday's child – of him no trace
Wednesday's child is full of woe
Thursday's child died long ago
Friday's child is standing and chiding
Saturday's child is running and hiding
And the child that is born on the Sabbath day
Curses God above for the bomb he gave.

Michael Donnelly

(AHEM) EXCUSE ME

(Ahem) Excuse me.
I never wanted atom bombs
but they didn't ask me anyway.
I never wanted two world wars
but I wasn't born then anyway.
I wasn't asked about things in Ulster,
I was the quiet one mumbling "Please sir."
My vote didn't count when it came to Angola.
I gave my opinion, but I don't think they heard.
It wasn't me who wanted Vietnam
but they didn't ask me anyway
and I never wanted Afghanistan
but they didn't ask me anyBLAM ...

Peter Astley

THINK CAREFULLY
BEFORE READING THIS

This is a bureaucratic poem.
Please sign (in block capitals)
in triplicate upon receipt.
Knock before entering.
Read the instructions carefully
(Do not exceed the stated dose).
Do not park on the nouns.
Do not walk on the consonants.
Do not spit on the vowels.
Do not recite loudly.
Please leave this poem in the
condition in which you find it.
Flush after use, and
DO NOT DO THAT.

Andrew Darlington

WEDDING DAY NURSERY CHRYME

Cooking beans and rinsing dishes,
wedding plans with the in-laws' wishes,
Hoovering carpets, Flash the kitchen,
supermarkets, clothes need stitching.

Baby foods and plastic cups,
soaking nappies, the washing-up.
Work and work to make ends meet,
make cold love once a week.

Knuckle down to the household chores,
fusing lights, unhinging doors.
Slapping paint on private houses,
scrubbing shirts and bleaching trousers.

Plates of Bird's Eye, mugs of tea,
this marrying lark's not for me.
'Cos now we're dodging rent 'n' rates,
and me I'm dodging cups and plates.

Settlements and bank accounts,
compensation – large amounts.
Sorry, girl, we'll see y'around,
a pocket full of money and we're off to town.

Boy passing through a different phase,
needs a change of girl with a different face.
Work and work, but now it's fun,
a wedding cake from now on.
Yeah!

Aidan Cant

48

Andy Bylo

LIFE STORY

am on other side of midnight with bed rehearsing
as understudy for the oven think about belsen
and roll over and try to sleep but by the time
the 4,000th jew has disappeared into the great
frying pan realize its not helping me sleep so
get up to make another cup of coffee stopping
off at toilet on the way go back to british gas
bed and think about masturbation but too close
to the edge because really need a friend not a
finger and dog keeps giving bored glances and
panting a lot which makes me nervous finally
creep into a dream before waking around noon
explore the possibilities of doing something
exciting decide imaginations fading because
excitement doesnt work when theres no one around
so take dog and imagination to the grass for a
wander around call on newspaper seller who mumbles
something vaguely friendly but ears and brain
dont tune to asian accent so rather than keep
saying pardon just try to smile but facial muscles
arent ready for the shock so it comes out awry
and face feels distorted so fall out to the sun
and get back to inspecting the grass come back
awake not necessarily alive sit coffee in hand
staring at the mess of living in a flat put on
highway 61 and inspect eyebrows in mirror which
dissolves in front of eyes and becomes the albert
hall sing a handful of songs say thankyou and
refuse to do any encores as side one fades out
fade back into mess in flat work out a list of
ways of putting it in order without getting
disordered again when finished decide its against

the laws of nature and instead invent conversation
with vacant chair about love and living chair
fails to see point so launch into argument again
decide next time just talk to myself and stop all
this friction flatmate comes in with friend so
chair and me resolve differences of opinion for
friends sake but only temporary status quo thats
for sure flatmate and friend getting private so
decided to try out womens room which doesnt allow
men in but lots of men there anyway think at least
here will fit in but after spending 3 hours being
a far gone leper propping up bar before legs
disappear decide its just another battle in my war
and am still on other side of midnight.

Claire Dowie

OUTER LIMITS

Change and time for it.
Your socks, my degree in domesticity.
A clean and tidy house, pleasure enough for me.
While your friends thought me charming,
you wished another behind my mask.

So I gave it you.

My lip. Sore from the bites.
Legs. Weak from the shackles, in need of rest.
I threw off my ball and chain to dance with you.
Your style, outrageous and extrovert,
being the other side, the one relatives were safe with,
the side that would not embarrass.

You felt left out. Alone.

So make way, woolly socks.
Time for slinky slips. In black of course.

Swearing at a bore's party,
shocking the host and kicking the cat.
Sarcastic to your mother,
would you be pleased at that?

I heard a filthy joke at the massage parlour,
the one I visit on Thursdays.
It's an "Irish, Scot and English" one.
I'm saving the punchline for your Christmas party.

Decided to return some cheese to Safeway's.
It stank.
Halted fellow shoppers as I tore the manager off a strip.
Got two free packs and an apology.
It pays to complain.

My life's certainly changed since you unlocked the door.
I feel much younger since I started this course.
I'm an individual now,
with no friends and a request from you for divorce.

Steve Wills

LIFE

There are pessimistic people,
those that cannot take
the pressures life hands out to them:
eventually they break.

There are those called optimistic —
I know for I am one;
we keep on fighting battles
as though they've just begun.

We take life as it's given
and strive from day to day;
all obstacles we challenge
as they stand in our way.

We have to run the gauntlet,
we conquer and we master,
and when the devil chases us
we carry on, but faster.

We battle through the night time,
we battle through the day,
we battle on regardless
for survival come what may.

But pessimistic people
think the rest of us are cruel,
for they are blind — they cannot see
survival is the rule.

The game of life just can't be bought,
the way is ours to choose,
so we must fight life's battlefield
(we'll fight it all our worth)
and when our lives are over
we'll have left our mark on earth . . .

Jordan Burgess Coates

DEATH AT THE DOG AND DUCK

born to run   run to race
race to death   last one six
feet under   buys the drinks
run for the bus   the tube the train
the plane the boat   run round the supermarket
quick service bolt food   keep running
chew settlers for   speedy relief
instant energy   junk food, pills
microwave ovens   and track shoes
cant stop, rush   keep running
cant afford a round   for the whole human race

wars declared   tight-fisted
or light weight   pocket people
rush for the front   up over past the
finishing line   set em up joe

      fella behinds payin
      fella behinds payin

bus tube train plane   boat fuller
cars streamlined   dodging breathalyser
clunk click   load of shit
smoke tug cough cancer   pub
starve blind coma death   pub
needles in arms   quick trip
forget pretty routes   cant afford the round

      fella behinds payin
      fella behinds payin

get the h bomb   (organized racing now)
goad em push em poke em   make them drop it
make them pay   yeah they can buy the round

      fella in the easts payin
      fella in the wests payin

euthanasia suicide   overworked heart
overused body   get it grab it take it use it
anything will do   got to rush got to run

      fella behind
      fella behind

Claire Dowie

THE LOVING

They kissed together one final time,
And felt the warmth of the afternoon chill.
Shadows falling from the leafless trees stumbled across
    the concrete.
He watched them thicken as neon flashed its dim blue eye
Above the traffic that honked into the cascade of the
    busy city.
Silence hung between them as fragile as her head on
    his shoulder.
As desperate as the beating of her heart.
They were both lost,
And they were both delaying the moment
When they would have to admit it.
There were no words.
And time for dreams had gone,
And gentle dreamers they were left washed up on the bleak
    beach of nightmares,
Waiting for night to tear them apart.
She murmured, as though in sleep.
He hugged her closer.
She looked at him like a child pretending to be someone else,
    somewhere else, in someone else's world.
A child on the eve of starting school.
Her smile trembled.
"It's time to go," he whispered.
Her eyes lowered, her lips determined not to speak
The thoughts that were a jumble of tears.
"I'll see you again?"
He nodded.

Liars both, they felt it easier
To live and lie
Than live and cry
Tears for the gathering shadow of sorrow;
A lethal cloud hovering.

A train roared,
A diesel stallion kicking up sparks
Rushing into the Absolute of the night.

A lonely station fell to the quiet of emptiness.

Nothing remained except for two tears
Falling into the eternity of regret.

David Fields

I FELL IN LOVE WITH A LIBRARIAN
(LOVE BETWEEN THE LINES)

54

You'll always be on order.
You'll never be overdue,
but when I tried to see you
I went to the back of the queue.

The only date I ever got off you
was one on the inside page.
I'd love to take you out at night,
soft lights, wine and dine,
but the only money I ever spent on you
was two 25p fines.

My love life without you
is like a Polo
without the hole
you're always in my fantasy
you take the leading role

My life, my times, my dreams of you
were always spent in fiction,
but you're a stupid boring little bitch
you always gave preference to reference.

So try, try as hard as I can
I cannot "cop off" with that librarian.
Some are only gem stones,
but you to me were a pearl.
I gave up chasing women
and went back to chasing girls.

John Hollingsworth

MELLIFLUENCE PARK AVE
(TO ABSENT FRIENDS)

Over-growing trees shadow a teenage dream,
a dream I found under the pillows of time.
This park so grey ... the starting rain,
and I wonder,
I wonder,
if she'll forever leave me suspended in the loneliest
    of places,
if she'll forever put the hood on me.
But she will be waiting, I'm sure,
under that old flickering gas lamp in the park;
where one can see wrinkled leaves being gently blown away
    down the dark path.
Absolutely pouring down with rain.
She never came, nor kept our time.
Vainly I waited ... waited ... and waited ...
until my body shivered with cold.

The girl with a pram ... passes by.
The man with the crooked walking stick ... passes by.
The faceless kid footballer ... passes by.
Stupid girl, you'd never come anyway,
you'll be crying for me some day,
then I'll be your absent friend.

Whistling vengeful bossa nova tunes to pass the long walk
    home away,
rusty bikes catch my eye.
Just like myself, waiting for an absent friend.
Goodbye 'til we meet again,
but I don't know where, and don't know when.

Aidan Cant

BUBBLES

I once had a love like sparkling champagne
That tickled my senses and teased my brain
Without her bubbles my life is as plain
As mud without puddles, sky without rain
O Lord, let me be drunk again.

James Kelly

ENCORE
UNE FOIS

Boyd Montgomery

I

The bus was ten minutes late. Rend felt himself crushed as the smaller bodies of the first- and second-years swarmed around him. He was tossed and turned by the rush. Eventually he managed to fight on board the bus and find a seat for himself. He was surrounded by workers. Real workers, not like himself a pen-pusher, head-stuck in books and easy life. Men who had to graft for a living, hard physical sweat. Rend could not help feeling that his life was shallow and had no use to others. He could sense the contempt the workers had for him. Kids his own age looked at him. Work had turned them into strong lads twice his size. There was an honesty about them and a deception about him.

– Well then, Rendy? asked Dem Junte in his usual sickly way of talking.

– She's looking nice, Rend replied.

This was the once a fortnight Newtown Association Youth Disco, where the youngsters were allowed to enjoy themselves, albeit under strictly controlled conditions – the don't you talk to any nasty boys and be back by ten o'clock or else you won't be allowed out on your own again because we remember what it was like when we were young and we don't want you doing any of the things we did. Rend and Dem were talking about Linda Jane Doliney whom Rend had been wanting to ask out for some time.

– Ask her to dance then, encouraged Dem, as ever keen to see Rend fall on his face and bomb out.

Rend hesitated and then walked over. His palms began to sweat and his mouth felt dry. He knew he would have difficulty speaking. Breaking the ice is the hardest part, he thought. After that it's all downhill.

– Wanna dance? he asked. Keep it short.

– If y'like.

They danced and talked for a bit. Rend found himself growing out of patter. He began to panic. Christ! say something. What? Anything.

– I'm tired, do you want to sit down?

– Alright.

This, then, was stage two. Having danced with the girl and asked her questions (you know, hobbies, boyfriends, popstars, anything like that), you sit together and then put your arm round her. It's easy for girls, they just have to sit there and look pretty, thought Rend. We do all the work. I wonder if they know the routine as well as we do. Do they enjoy it? I expect they must.

Linda was looking away, waiting for Rend to begin.

Christ. I can't. I want to talk to her. I want to tell her what I think about life. I don't want to maul all over her. She's a person too. The expected reactions. Sex and lust. Go on lad, all the lads chase the birds. What's she thinking now? Problem of communication. Christ I'm sweating. Oh God, what a state. All this flashed through Rend's brain in an instant. He reached a decision.

– Come on, let's go. He snatched her hand and pulled her up.

– What! she exclaimed.

– We're leaving, Rend replied, pulling her towards the exit. Linda followed obediently. He had caught her off-balance. Nobody had ever tried this tack with her before. On the way out she grabbed her coat. Rend was glad to be out in the open, free from the noise and the heat.

– I'm sorry, he said. I just couldn't stand it in there. It's much nicer out here.

– Well, you're a one, I must say.

Rend smiled at Linda

— I just didn't know what to do. I panicked and here we are. He paused. He felt more relaxed now. His earlier fear was gone. What did it matter what he did and said? So long as he was honest he had nothing to fear. But this was only a temporary joy. Linda did not care for him and quite frankly could not care if she never saw him again.

— Do you want to walk a bit? he said.

— Might as well. I was going home anyway.

Rend walked Linda home, during which time he discovered she was not interested in him. Walking back home later on Rend stopped awhile and listened to the sound of his own breathing. It was quiet now, Rend was on his own. He was tired. It was dark and silent. It was cold too. He wanted to sit down and rest. The sounds of that evening flooded his mind. The sensations came back to him. He recalled everything he had said. Some of it made him squirm with embarrassment. Still it's very easy to be clever in hindsight. There's no point in getting worked up about that. I think I said what was right or what I thought was right. I mean what else can you do? No man has any right to expect anyone else to be perfect (to aspire to it, yes, but never to achieve it). He listened to the silence. Oh Christ please let me get through just one more day. Just one more round of repetition, rejection, repression, repulsion.

▮▮

Two old tramps were standing next to each other on the corner of an old run-down warehouse. Old torn posters peeled off the walls and there was a heavy smell of creosote and rust. Too apathetic to do anything, too apathetic to move. The air was weighed down with an atmosphere. An old scraggy mongrel cocked its leg and pissed on a poster which read TODAY'S GIRL USES XO DEODORANTS FOR ALL-ROUND PERSONAL FRESHNESS in large yellow letters accompanied by a photo of the type of girl who always appears in these sorts of posters, a plastic face and painted smile. A pile of newspapers were turning brown alongside a collection of other pieces of discarded rubbish. The newspapers told of individuals and public issues, full of people who once had a brief glimpse of fame with 'their photos in the paper' and then returned to the humiliating grind and drudge of their daily lives. The people were long dead and their photos and stories were turning grey. The journalists who had hounded their victims for their stories and then stayed up late typing the reports, wasting their lives looking for that big break that would make their name, they too were gone. What did it matter now that they had forgotten things and failed in others? What did it matter?

One of the newspaper stories told of a girl who was a talented piano player. She had told her friends she wanted to know what it was like to die but they just thought she was joking. Then one day she went down to the London to Edinburgh railway line which ran near her house and put her head on the track and waited for a train to come along. She was sixteen. Her parents could not understand what made her do such a thing. The newspaper article was accompanied by a photo of her smiling, happy. The photo was turning brown.

One of the tramps took from a plastic bag a bottle of brown ale and took a big swig from it. His name was Tom. His days and nights were spent in an alcoholic daze on the banks of the T–. The T– Bridge loomed ominously over his head, the occasional car rumbled over. It was bloody cold, thought Tom. He was bloody freezing. His friend stared vacantly at the T–. It began small up on the fells of N– and grew on its path down to the sea. Like a life which is born small. All lives are born alike, and then either grow large or fade out or end in sudden violence.

The tramps dirty and scraggy and smelly. Tom's friend had a history of mental illness. He was simple, a child. Tom had been unwanted, unloved. He looked after his friend, since his friend needed him. Tom did not realize it but he needed his friend as well. Looking after him gave Tom a reason to continue. His friend coughed and spluttered and saliva dribbled on to his beard. Tom helped him wipe it off. What his name was Tom did not know. But since he had never called anyone by their name anyway Tom could not care. Tom was tired. He finished the brown ale and then threw the bottle in the river before settling down to sleep. The bottle bobbed about in the dirty grey water before being carried down stream and then out to sea....

On Saturday, 27 June 195– Jack and Maria Donnelly went to a dance at the Oxford Tea-Rooms on Prosage Street. (Thus scene is set in an acknowledged location within infinity, identification of a time and place, well, almost.) The Oxford was a large ornate building. It reminded Maria of the Theatre, where she used to see pantomines when she was young and where a studious young man she used to date took her to see a performance of King Lear by Mr William Shakespeare. She had hated that; it was such an awful story and anyway you could not understand what they were saying half of the time since they all talked old-fashioned and funny. The Tea-Rooms reminded her of the Theatre in that there were a couple of steps leading up and there was a man in uniform on the door who took your tickets off you and touched the top of his cap and bowed in respect to the ladies. Maria had liked that; it was respectful and gentlemanly. Jack could be like that too at times, when he felt like it. The Tea-Rooms had a foyer where you could stand and talk to friends or, if you preferred, go straight through the double doors and out into the dancing area. Maria liked going out to dos like these. She enjoyed taking her time getting dressed and everything. She hoped her friends were there so they could see how fine she looked. She had bought herself a new dress only two days earlier. Jack went scatty when he found out, calling her all sorts of names, spending his hard-earned money like that. She knew they could barely afford it and that it would be her last new thing for a while but just for tonight she did not care. She wanted to start dancing straight away but Jack wanted to have a drink first and so she went over to the bar with him. No sooner had they got their drinks but Paul Rend came over and started to talk to Jack whilst Maria just stood listening to their conversation and smiling occasionally. Presently Paul's girlfriend, Clare, came over and Maria started to talk to her.

Both Clare and Maria soon became restless and so pulled Jack and Paul away from the bar and on to the dance floor. They knew they'd better get their dances in early on before the men had too much to drink. They milled around the floor with the other couples, occasionally bumping into someone, turning round and recognizing a familiar face. Maria like being in Jack's arms. He was not physically strong but he gave her a sense of security. He knew his own mind. So did she, mind you, and he was no way going to force her to do something she did not want to. Like the time he wanted her to suck his thing. She said she'd never heard to such a thing (she had though) and that she was sure it was a sin to do anything as unnatural. He said it was not a sin because they were married and that it would be a beautiful experience. She said it might be beautiful for him but what about her getting a mouthful of his sticky stuff, the very thought made her feel sick. Despite that, she knew that with Jack she had a man for life. He was dependable, she'd say that for him. If he said he'd do something, then he'd do it. She was lucky to have him. Not like Pauline Doliney. Her husband soon buggered off and left her with two kids to raise. Terrible thing that. A man should face his responsibilities and that included looking after his woman. But she knew she was all right with Jack. He did not have the same effect on her as Cary Grant, mind. She remembered one time she was looking at his photo and she began to dream about him kissing her and she got an itch between her legs and began to scratch and before she knew where she was, she was in raptures as waves of joy flooded over her (real woman's drama stuff, this). Afterwards she felt awful about being so shameless and, since she knew it was a sin, wanted to tell Father Farrow about it in confession. But she could not pluck up enough courage, so she went to a different church where she did not know the priest and confessed in a very small voice that she had played with herself. The priest told here that such urges were understandable but she must resist them and say three Hail Marys and promise not to do it again. Jack had never made her want to play with herself. All the same she sometimes used to get the itchy feeling when they were making babies, though at other times she just used to act as if she were enjoying it so as not to hurt Jack's feelings. Trouble was, she never got pregnant. Although they could hardly afford kids, she did so want one of her own. She thought Jack might be, you know, it sounds like 'important' and means you can't make a baby. Some of the girls at her old school had told her that was when the man couldn't get it stiff, but Jack had no trouble there, so he couldn't be a potent after all. She remembered after she had done it with Brian she thought she was pregnant and got terribly worried about having to bring up a baby that was not her husband's, but that turned out to be a false alarm. Still, for tonight she was not going to worry about not having a baby. Who knows, when they got home perhaps they could have another go, if Jack did not get too drunk, that is. As they went around Maria felt really happy. She was really quite lucky. She had a nice home, a good husband, and here she was at the Oxford Tea-Rooms dancing in a brand-new dress. Who could ask for anything more than that? Really.

IV

OK so let's just stop and see what we've got here. I don't think we need any kitchen-sink opera-type drama, interplay of characters schmuck. We're looking for a new prose here. I mean we've got to work this thing together, I mean I know you want the story and the twists of plot but anyone can do that. We've got to look for something more special. I mean if you want a good story then you should read Tom Jones, all other story books are pretty much alike. Of course there's always hack-filth of third-rate garbage spewed out by despair merchants, you know handsome crew-cut square-jawed hero (brain surgeon, wine expert, ex-commando, concert violinist) combats international underworld and is like on Spanish fly always having it off with sophisticated, suntanned 42″ bust. 'But it's entertainment, man'. Ok, but it doesn't have to be brainless, no-hope drivel. Or you've got the menopausal syndrome, with you know the middle-aged reaching crises in their lives. I tell you, friend, it's their own fault. They made the decision to devote their lives to a firm's profit instead of thinking about God's free joys.

You know, it's like a closed syndrome, all these writers. They all know each other and go to the same literary receptions and evenings and send each other postcards. But really it's like Joyce said, the true artist must be an exile and must work on his own with only stealth and cunning to guide him, but I'd add faith and courage to that. You must believe in what you are doing.

Stephen Earl